BOOK

Printed and Published in Great Britain by D. C. THOMSON & CO., LTD., 185 Fleet Street, London EC4A 2HS.
ISBN 0 85116 270 3

DESPERATE DAN
YOU'LL NEVER GUESS HOW THIS CAME ABOUT! READ ON TO FIND OUT!
RUMBLE

The bullfight ends—

THANKS, DAN! THAT WAS MY BEST SHOW EVER.

Then—

HEY, DAN! TWO BANDITS HAVE JUST STOLEN THE TAKINGS.

THERE THEY GO, DAN!

LEAVE 'EM TO ME, SHERIFF!

RIGHT! LET'S GET AFTER THEM, HOPALONG!

QUICK! DODGE INTO THIS OLD BARN!

SO, THEY'RE HIDING IN THAT BARN, EH? GET YOUR HEAD DOWN, HOPALONG, AND WE'LL SOON ROUST THEM OUT.

BERTIE BUNCLE
AND HIS CHEMICAL UNCLE

PHEW! THE GRASS IS TOO LONG FOR THE LAWNMOWER. THERE MUST BE AN EASIER WAY!

YOU PROMISED TO CUT THE GRASS LAST WEEK, BERTIE, AND YOU DIDN'T! SO GET IT DONE NOW!

OH, ALL RIGHT, UNCLE BUNCLE!

WONDER IF THERE'S ANYTHING IN UNCLE'S LAB THAT WOULD HELP?

YUMMY! SMASHING! IT'S FAR TOO TASTY! MUNCH!

WHAT'S UP, UNCLE BUNCLE?

I'VE MADE A NEW KIND OF FOOD, BERTIE. IT'S SO TASTY I CAN'T RESIST IT MYSELF. QUICK! TAKE IT AWAY AND DESTROY IT!

I HAVE A PLAN.

I'LL SCATTER THIS STUFF ALL OVER THE LONG GRASS!

THEN I'LL INVITE SOME OF MY PALS TO TASTE IT!

...THEY'LL LIKE IT SO MUCH THAT THEY'LL MUNCH UP ALL THE GRASS—JUST LIKE A FLOCK OF SHEEP! HO-HO!

BRASSNECK

C RICKET, tennis, football, any sport at all—Brassneck, the metal marvel, can play them better than any superstar. The brass boy has an electric brainbox and mechanical innards that make him walk and talk like any other boy, and he can also do lots more too.

Everyone thinks he is smashing fun—except teacher, Fatso Snodgrass. And you can find out how the metal marvel turned the grumpy master into a nervous wreck in this story—

Brassneck's next shot at goal was even harder.

THUD!

YIKE! I'M GETTING OUT OF HERE BEFORE THE WHOLE PLACE COLLAPSES!

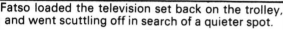

Fatso loaded the television set back on the trolley, and went scuttling off in search of a quieter spot.

NOW WHERE CAN I GO?

STORE

Soon he came upon the very place.

THE OLD CLOCK TOWER! NO ONE EVER GOES UP THERE! THE CLOCK'S BEEN BROKEN FOR YEARS!

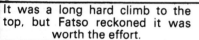

It was a long hard climb to the top, but Fatso reckoned it was worth the effort.

I WON'T BE DISTURBED UP HERE!

At that very moment, however, someone WAS disturbing the boys.

YOU KNOW THE RULES! NO FOOTBALL ALLOWED IN THE PLAYGROUND!

YES, MR JENKINS!

The bad-tempered janitor confiscated Charley's football, but the lads weren't beaten yet.

DON'T WORRY, BRASSNECK! WE CAN PLAY FOOTER WITH THIS TENNIS BALL!

As soon as Oddjob Jenkins had gone, the game restarted.

MY BALL!

And it wasn't long before Brassneck gave the small ball a big kick.

AND HE SHOOTS FOR GOAL... *OOPS!*

The ball flew skywards and the hand that stopped it belonged to no goalie, but to the school clock.

It was then that Brassneck did an amazing thing. With the aid of his special suction feet he walked straight up the wall of the clock tower.

BRASSNECK WILL SOON GET THE BALL BACK!

But retrieving the ball meant moving the hand of the clock forward. And when that hand reached the hour . . .

DONG!

The deafening din almost made Fatso jump out of his skin.

WHAT ON EARTH!

DONG!

. . . the bell sounded again . . .

OOH! THE CLOCK'S STARTED UP! JUST MY LUCK!

Fatso grabbed the television set and galloped away from the ear-splitting racket.

DONG!

MUST GET OUT OF HERE! CAN'T STAND THAT NOISE!

He didn't stop running till he reached the very last step of the clock tower stairs.

GASP! MUST FIND SOMEWHERE ELSE TO WATCH THE MATCH!

The master headed back into the school.

SCIENCE LAB.

I SHOULD BE SAFER HERE.

The science lab was just the spot. It was empty for the present.

. . . AND JONES PASSES TO ALLEN . . .

Meanwhile, the boys decided to have a change of game. Brassneck fetched some suitable equipment from the school kitchens.

ANYONE FOR TENNIS?

The brass boy had another bright idea.

WE CAN USE THESE BINS INSTEAD OF A NET!

Soon the game was in full swing.

HOW'S THAT FOR A SMASH?

Another SMASH followed when Brassneck walloped the ball straight through the science lab window.

CRASH!

REACHED IT! ... OH, NO!

GULP! THAT'S TORN IT.

The ball whistled past Fatso's nose . . .

. . . hit some bottles full of chemicals . . .

. . . and sent them crashing into the sink.

The chemicals mixed together and created a horrible pong.

The smell was so strong that the teacher had to move on with his TV set once again.

Fatso was running out of places to take his telly.

SHOULD BE QUIET IN HERE!

SCHOOL KITCHEN

Meanwhile, the boys went to look in the lab for their ball.

SCIENCE LAB

They had to retreat from the nasty niff.

UGH! WHAT A SMELL!

SCIENCE LAB.

No one could figure out what had happened, but the boys agreed about one thing.

LET'S GET AWAY FROM HERE BEFORE WE'RE BLAMED FOR CAUSING THAT SMELL!

GOOD THINKING, BRASSNECK. LET'S GO, LADS!

They headed for the far side of the playground, and since Fatso was nowhere to be seen, one of Charley's classmates had an idea!

FANCY A GAME OF CRICKET?

YOU BET!

Moments later, the game started, and look who was first into bat!

TRY THIS ONE FOR SIZE, BRASSNECK!

WHACK! The brass boy had no trouble hitting the ball, but the fielder wasn't first eleven material.

SCHOOL KITCHEN

CRASH!

I'VE HIT A SIX!

CRUMBS! FATSO WILL HIT US FOR SIX WHEN HE SEES THAT WINDOW!

But it was poor Fatso who was hit for six! His telly-viewing seat was right in the cricket ball's flight-path.

BONK!

UMMFF!

The boys could hardly believe their eyes when they rushed into the kitchen.

SCHOOL KITCHEN

LOOK, SIR! FATSO... ER, I MEAN, MR SNODGRASS HAS FAINTED OR SOMETHING.

HOW AWFUL! I'LL CALL AN AMBULANCE!

Charley wheeled Fatso outside.

With Fatso out of action, the Headmaster gave Charley's class the rest of the day off. And the lads knew exactly where to spend it—back in the school kitchen. There they could watch the football match on TV, and have lots of grub on hand, too.

IZZY SKINT

HE ALWAYS IS!

ALLOW ME!

SNATCH!

HEY! IT'S BILLY BARNETT!

I'M NOT SKINT TODAY! I'VE GOT FIFTY PENCE OF MY CHRISTMAS MONEY. HEADS I BUY FRUIT DROPS, TAILS I BUY CHOCOLATE.

TOSS!

IT'S HEADS FOR FRUIT DROPS—'COS THAT'S WHAT I LIKE. HA-HA!

WHUMP!

OOF!

NOW I'LL NIP DOWN TO THE PARK AND EAT THIS BIG BAG OF BOILED SWEETS!

GURR! I'LL FOLLOW HIM AND GET EVEN!

I THINK I'LL START WITH AN ORANGE ONE.

HERE'S MY CHANCE!

URP! IZZY DOESN'T KNOW WHAT HE'S MISSING!

TH-WHACK!

HA-HA! WELL, I DIDN'T MISS HIM!

SWISH!

OOYAH!

GURR!

THANKS FOR RETURNING MY SWEETS, BILLY!

BILLY WON'T GIVE UP EASILY SO I'LL PUT THE SWEETS IN MY POCKETS AND FILL THE BAG WITH THESE STONES—JUST IN CASE!

HEE-HEE! THIS REALLY DOES LOOK LIKE A BAG OF SWEETS.

HAND BACK THAT BAG OF SWEETS, IZZY—OR ELSE!

OKAY, BILLY!

HELLO, BILLY. HOW ABOUT GIVING ME A SWEET?

OO-ER! BILLY'S MET UP WITH GRASPER GRIMSHAW.

ULP! CERTAINLY, GRASPER! PLEASE TAKE ONE!

ONE HANDFUL, OF COURSE!

ONE HANDFUL WILL JUST ABOUT FILL MY MOUTH. HEH-HEH!

CRACK! CRUNCH!

HO-HO! HEADS YOU LOSE, BILLY!

GURR! A PRANKSTER, EH?

BIFF! BON

TWENTIETH CENTURY CAT PRESENTS —

~~GONE WITH THE WIND~~ starring **DESPERATE DAN**

TISHOO!

WOOSH!

CRASH!

PRODUCED BY **SNEEZING POWDER**

The "CAINE" MUTINY
STARRING WINKER WATSON

WHACK!
WHACK!

The "BIG-HIT" MOVIE

For Whom The Bell Tolls
STARRING **THE SMASHER**

SWISH!

SOUND EFFECTS PRODUCED BY **MR THRASHER**

The **GREAT ESCAPE**
STARRING PETER'S POCKET GRANDPA

And introducing
TIDDLES

MADCAP MOVIES

STAR WARS
Continuous Performances from 4 p.m. daily

STARRING THE JOCKS AND THE GEORDIES

Goodbye Mr Chips
STUNT MAN — BULLY BEEF
STUNTED MAN — CHIPS

BOOT!

BREAKFAST AT TIFFANY'S
(ALSO LUNCH, DINNER, TEA AND MID-MORNING SNACKS)

STARRING **TOM TUM** AND A CAST OF THOUSANDS OF WAITERS

Black Beauty
STARRING BULLY BEEF
(X CERTIFICATE)

WHAT'S NEW PUSSYCAT?

SUPER FUN TALES FROM DESPERATE DAN, THE SMASHER, BULLY BEEF, WINKER WATSON AND THE JOCKS AND THE GEORDIES IN **THE DANDY** COMIC EVERY WEEK!

STARRING **KORKY** the **CAT**

The BYRD-BRAINS

BERTRAM

IN 1903 IN AMERICA, THE WRIGHT BROTHERS MADE THE FIRST POWERED FLIGHT, AND PAVED THE WAY FOR THE AIRCRAFT WE KNOW TODAY. BUT IN A QUIET ENGLISH VILLAGE TWO OTHER BROTHERS WERE ALSO TRYING TO FLY. THEY WERE BERTRAM AND BREWSTER BYRD-BRAIN.

BREWSTER

ONE OF THE BROTHERS' EARLIEST ATTEMPTS TO FLY WAS BY USING A PAIR OF ROCKET BOOTS. BERTRAM PUT THEM ON.

BUT THEY HAD BOUGHT CHEAP ROCKETS, AND ONE FIZZLED OUT.

AND INSTEAD OF A FLIGHT THROUGH THE SKY, BERTRAM...

... WENT FOR A SPIN IN THE COUNTRY.

PETER'S POCKET GRANDPA

Peter Parker's Grandpa came off worst in an argument with a strange gipsy. The gipsy lost his temper and shrank Grandpa to midget size!

In a big High Street store—

HUH! I'M FED UP OF ALL THIS CHRISTMAS SHOPPING, PETER.

In the toy department—

GOSH! I WOULD LIKE TO JOIN IN THAT GAME, PETER.

So—

GREAT SAVE, GRANDPA!

CLICK!

ZOOM

YOU GO AHEAD AND FINISH YOUR SHOPPING. I'LL JOIN YOU LATER AT THE CAR.

OKAY, GRANDPA.

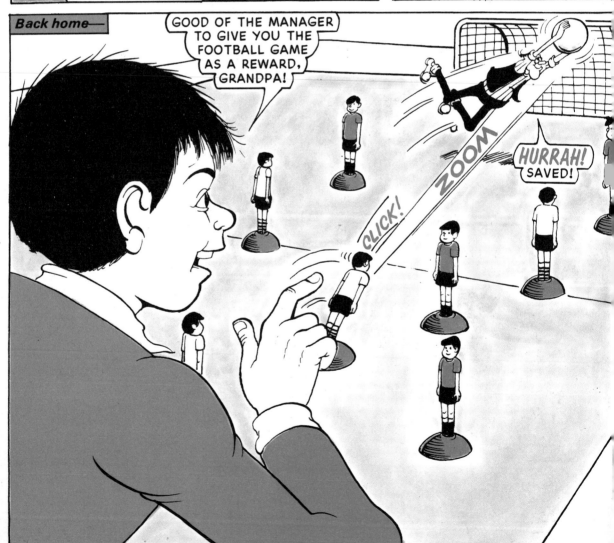

HARRY and his HIPPO

OVER THERE, HANDSOME PET OF MINE!

BEST LOOKING PET SECTION →

BEST LOOKING SECTION

GURR!

...MM! I MUST ...TER HIPPO ...OR THIS.

TOWN HALL

PET SHOW TODAY PRIZES FOR ALL CLASSES OF PETS

TAKE THAT DREADFUL CREATURE AWAY!

JUDGE

HUH!

CLEVEREST PET SECTION →

THAT'S MORE IN YOUR LINE, HIPPO!

CLEAR OFF, FATTY!

CLEVEREST PET SECTION

EH?

CLEVEREST PET SECTION

HO-HO! VERY CLEVER— FIRST PRIZE TO YOU!

JUDGE

...xt—

MOST UNUSUAL PET →

HERE'S WHAT I'LL ENTER YOU FOR!

BOUND

UNUSUAL PETS HERE!

SQUEAL!

ERK!

YIKE!

WORMS

The FLYING BOY of WOOMERA

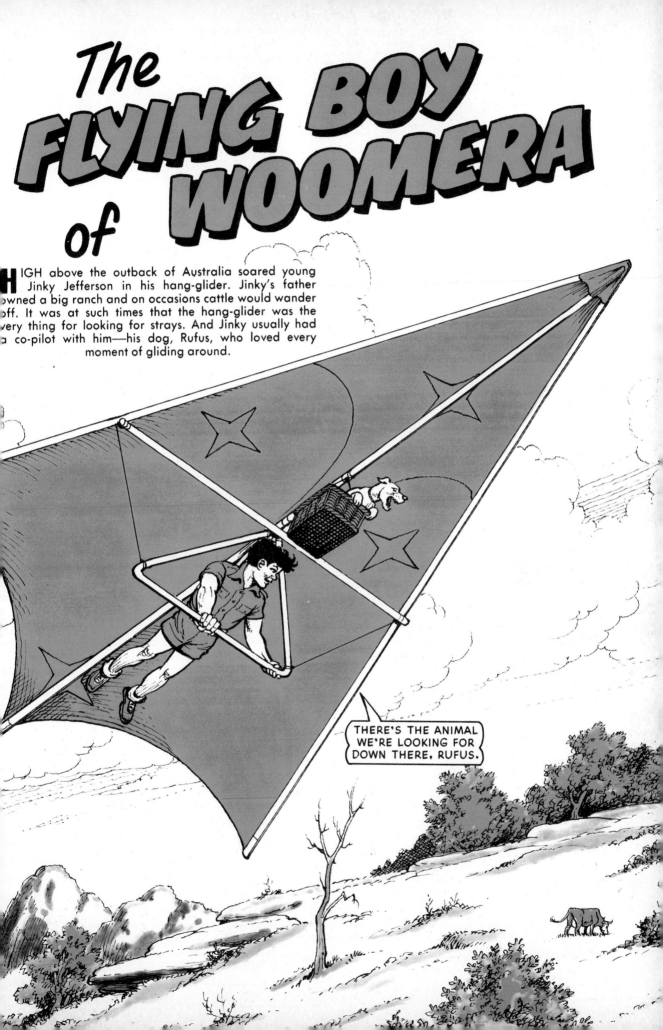

HIGH above the outback of Australia soared young Jinky Jefferson in his hang-glider. Jinky's father owned a big ranch and on occasions cattle would wander off. It was at such times that the hang-glider was the very thing for looking for strays. And Jinky usually had a co-pilot with him—his dog, Rufus, who loved every moment of gliding around.

THERE'S THE ANIMAL WE'RE LOOKING FOR DOWN THERE, RUFUS.

Jinky was dazed and the hang-glider dipped out of control.

THUD! All of a sudden a boomerang struck Jinky a blow on the forehead.

OOF!

The boy regained his senses just in time to make an emergency landing.

Badly frightened, Rufus scampered off into the scrub.

HEY! COME BACK, RUFUS!

Then Jinky spotted a strange jeep in a copse.

WHOSE JEEP IS THAT, I WONDER?

He crept closer and came upon two men using metal detectors.

hen a hand grabbed Jinky by the shoulder.

It was an aborigine, the same fellow who had thrown the boomerang. He was in league with the two men with the metal detectors.

WE'LL HAVE TO TIE HIM UP, WHILE WE GET ON WITH OUR SEARCH.

Jinky was left propped against a rock while the two men continued their search.

Presently Jinky heard a rustle in the bushes behind him. It was Rufus who had recovered from his fright.

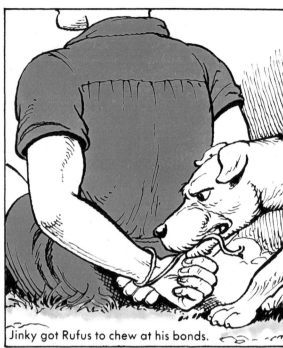

Jinky got Rufus to chew at his bonds.

The searchers were so intent on their work that they failed to notice the boy and the dog scurrying off.

But he had to move it to higher ground for take-off. By now, the aborigine was hard on their trail.

Jinky returned to his hang-glider.

IT'S STILL IN WORKING ORDER.

COME ON, RUFUS. WE'LL HAVE TO BE QUICK.

MADE IT!

Jinky flung himself off a rocky outcrop, seconds before the aborigine caught up with them.

Soaring free, Jinky spotted groups of kangaroos below and they gave him an idea.

YIP-YIP!
WOO-WOO—

Whooping and yelling, Jinky rounded up the kangaroos and headed them in the direction of the copse where the strangers were searching.

On came the kangaroos, faster and faster, as panic spread among them. And it was a jostling pack of fear-crazed animals by the time the stampede reached the copse. The kangaroos came bouncing and leaping into the strangers' encampment, flattening everything in their path. The two men were knocked to the ground and badly trampled on.

Jinky landed in the wake of the stampede.

Quickly he tied up the bruised and dazed men before they recovered.

NOW IT'S MY TURN TO TIE YOU UP.

Then Rufus began to dig furiously.

WHAT'S THAT YOU'VE FOUND, RUFUS?

Jinky enlarged the hole and made an amazing discovery.

GOSH! A CHEST FULL OF GOLD COINS!

At length the police arrived and took away the two men. The inspector explained that the villains had stolen a map from a museum and it had led them to Ned Kelly's Treasure. The Australian bush ranger had buried it there over one hundred years before.

AND WE'LL ROUND UP YOUR ABORIGINE PAL LATER.

WELL DONE, JINKY! YOU'LL GET THE REWARD MONEY FOR THESE TWO.

BERTIE BUNCLE
AND HIS CHEMICAL UNCLE

THERE'S A WASP! LET ME SEE IF UNCLE BUNCLE'S SPRAY IS AS GOOD AS HE SAYS.

I'VE JUST INVENTED THIS MIXTURE FOR CHASING AWAY WASPS. GO AND TRY IT OUT IN THE GARDEN, BERTIE.

ALL RIGHT, UNCLE BUNCLE!

AARGH! UNCLE WAS WRONG! WASPS DON'T HATE IT! IN FACT, THEY SEEM TO LOVE IT!

I SUPPOSE I COULD HAVE GREAT FUN WITH THIS— IF I EVER GET OUT OF HERE!

Later—

THEY WENT AWAY AT LAST, THANK GOODNESS!

HEY! WHAT ARE YOU DOING, BUNCLE?

MAKING YOU BUZZ OFF, THAT'S ALL!

DEAR, DEAR! HE'S RUSHED AWAY AND LEFT ALL HIS SANDWICHES LYING ON THE BENCH!

HELP!

NO POINT IN WASTING GOOD FOOD! SLURP!

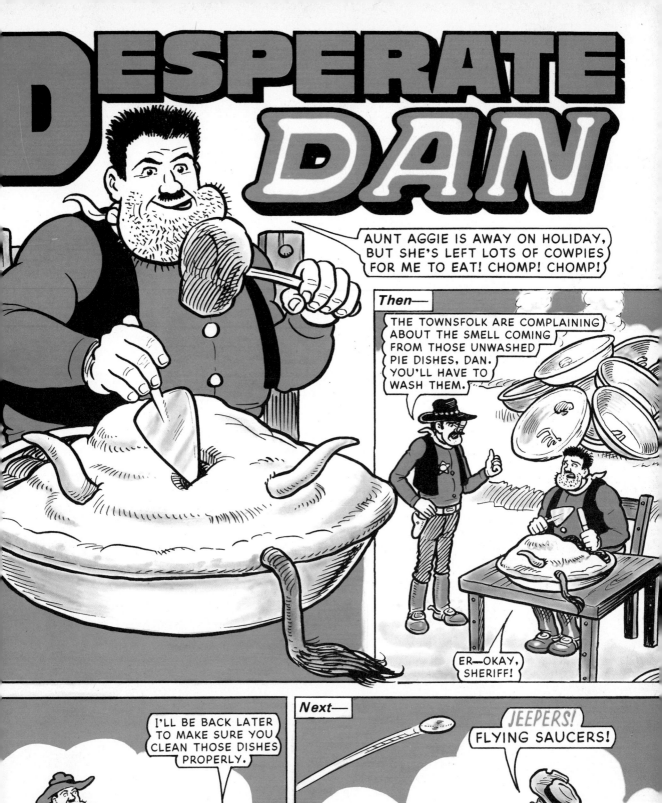

Winker Watson

EVERY boy loves a visit to the circus, but Winker Watson and his pal Tim Trott are luckier than most, because a circus is visiting them. On open ground next to Greytowers school, Chippendale's circus has set up its winter camp, and the pupils can watch the acts rehearse any time they choose.

CIRC

Well almost any time, because the boys also had lessons to attend and their teacher was Mr Creep, who made sure Winker Watson and his classmates had plenty of work to do.

SETTLE DOWN AND TAKE OUT YOUR HISTORY BOOKS . . .

All of a sudden . . .

THE FIRE BELL, SIR! MUST BE A FIRE DRILL!

RIGHT, BOYS! FILE OUT OF THE SCHOOL IN AN ORDERLY MANNER!

DRINNG!

Outside, the class was met by a breathless circus hand.

GASP! . . . ONE OF THE CIRCUS LIONS HAS ESCAPED! IT WAS SEEN HEADING TOWARDS THE SCHOOL PLAYGROUND

Mr Creep didn't like anything interfering with school work so he stomped off huffily, ignoring the circus man's warning.

STAND OVER BY THE CIRCUS VANS, BOYS, TILL WE CATCH THAT LION!

WHAT A NEEDLESS FUSS! I'M GOING BACK TO MY ROOM TO DO SOME WORK!

SCHOOL

At the circus camp, Winker met Micki, his circus pal.

LISTEN, MICKI, I'VE THOUGHT OF A WAY TO TRAP THAT LION!

And the circus cold store provided the "bait" Winker needed.

THIS JOINT OF BEEF WILL DO NICELY!

COLD STOR
KEEP OUT

Lots of schoolboys have catapults, but not many are as big as the one Micki and Winker made from a length of hosepipe and two bendy sapplings.

NOW TO SEND THE LION HIS LUNCH!

TWAANG!

GREYTOWERS SCHOOL

ROAR!

The meat hurtled through the air, right over the hungry lion's head and shot in at one of the school's open windows.

The big cat didn't wait for the school dinner bell to ring. He just sprang inside for a feed.

And once inside, he wasn't alone, for the lion had landed in Creepy's classroom.

Winker and Micki heard the lion's roars AND the master's squeals for help.

Micki had seen Leopold heading towards town in a circus van earlier in the day. Now the two boys cycled off to track him down.

The lads were in luck! One of the first places they came to was the local scrap-yard, and guess who was there!

The lion-tamer was far from pleased when Winker and Micki interrupted his business.

A LION'S ESCAPED! YOU'LL HAVE TO COME BACK AT ONCE!

HMPH! I SUPPOSE I WILL!

Back at the school, Creepy only came down from his perch on the light after the lion was safely rounded up.

IT'S STARTING TO RAIN! I'D BETTER GET THE BOYS BACK INTO CLASS!

COME ALONG, BOYS! YOU'LL BE NICE AND DRY INSIDE!

But Creepy's classroom was far from dry!

YIKE! THE CEILING IS LEAKING AND THE WHOLE ROOM IS SAILING IN WATER!

A quick glance at the school roof was all Creepy needed to discover the cause of the leaks.

ERK! SOMEONE'S STOLEN THE LEAD FROM THE ROOF!

I SAW LEOPOLD, THE LION-TAMER RECEIVING MONEY FROM A SCRAP DEALER. HE MUST BE THE THIEF!

And that "somewhere" was the circus BIG TOP! The boys thought it was great fun to study while the circus acts rehearsed. In fact there was only one long face in the whole giant tent—and that belonged to Mr Creep. Once again the boys of Greytowers had Winker Watson to thank for coming out tops.

JACK SILVER

JACK SILVER

CURLY PERKINS

HIGH STREET

PASSERS-BY stared in disbelief, children laughed their heads off, and drivers screeched to a halt, as a giant Christmas tree RAN down the High Street, with the strangest-looking passenger on board.

What the gaping townsfolk didn't know was that the tree was in fact a weird space creature and the figure clinging to its branches was really Captain Zapp, a master criminal from the far-off world of Marsuvia.

Our story begins earlier that same day, when Earth-boy, Curly Perkin and his Marsuvian pal, Jack Silver, were bringing a Christmas tree hom to Curly's house. The boys were in a happy mood for they had no ide they were being watched by the evil Captain Zapp.

SO YOU PUT THIS TREE IN YOUR LIVING ROOM, CURLY? *ZEH-HEH!* SOUNDS LIKE FUN!

YES, JACK! I'M SURE YOU'LL ENJOY SPENDINC CHRISTMAS ON EARTH!

Zapp hurried back to his space-ship, which was parked in an out of the way spot.

ZAW-HAW! NOW I KNOW HOW TO DEAL WITH THOSE BRATS!

Jack and Curly had helped put Zapp in jail back on Marsuvia but he had escaped and was now out for revenge.

MY DUPLICATOR MACHINE WILL FIX THEM!

DUPLICATOR

Zapp's clever gadget coul make a life-size copy c almost anything, so th bandit fed in a picture of tree-like creature . . . an minutes later the beast an its master were sneakin into Curly's garden.

MY TREE MONSTER LOOKS JUST LIKE THE EARTH FOOLS' CHRISTMAS TREE! NOW TO PUT IT IN THEIR HOUSE!

The creature knew the game was up, and made a run for it!

QUICK! DON'T LET IT GET AWAY!

Outside, Captain Zapp had been hovering on his space scooter, and now monster and master made off.

IT'S CAPTAIN ZAPP! I SHOULD HAVE KNOWN!

MY RAY GUN WILL STOP THEM, CURLY!

LEVEL CROSSING

CRACK!

It did! The flash activated the level crossing gate and the barrier crashed down in the runaways' path.

CRASH!

But Zapp had no intention of giving up.

SEND THOSE KIDS PACKING!

The tree monster arched back then twanged forward catapulting the parcels and baubles from its branches towards Jack and Curly.

OWCH!

OW!

While the boys dodged the barrage of gifts, Zapp clambered on to the creature.

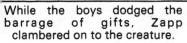

ZAH! MY SCOOTER'S OUT OF ACTION!

The space villain rapped out a command and the tree monster galloped off at an amazing speed.

YOU'LL PAY FOR THIS, YOU BRATS!

Travelling by lightning-fast tree wasn't comfy, but soon . . .

ZAPP'S GIVEN US THE SLIP!

NEVER MIND! I'LL SHOW YOU ANOTHER CHRISTMAS CUSTOM, JACK!

Curly took Jack carol-singing, but one of the first people to hear them was no music-lover.

WHILE SHEPHERDS WATCHED THEIR FLOCKS BY NIGHT . . .

ZAH! WHAT'S GOING ON?

One thing Captain Zapp DID love was cash. And his eyes almost popped out of his head when he saw Jack and Curly's reward.

LOVELY SINGING, BOYS! HERE'S SOMETHING FOR YOU!

THANK YOU, SIR!

The greedy bandit scurried back to his duplicator, eager to earn some cash.

IN GOES A PICTURE...

DUPLICATOR

...AND OUT COMES A COOTCHIE-COOTCHIE SONGBIRD!

The bird had an ugly mug but Captain Zapp knew its voice was beautiful...

... so he took up position outside a house, hoping the Songbird's trilling tones would make him rich.

COOTCHIE... COO-COO...

But Jack and Curly weren't far away.

LISTEN! THAT'S A MARSUVIAN COOTCHIE-COOTCHIE SONGBIRD!

The boys knew the bird could only belong to one man, and they soon tracked him down.

CRASH!

FIZZZZ!

ZAAEEEOOH!

Then a blast from Jack's ray gun turned the Cootchie Cootchie Bird's song into an ear-splitting SQUAWK!

BULL'S-EYE, JACK!

That high-pitched scream had a shattering effect on the windows of the house.

ZULP!

HEY, BALDY! DID YOU AND YOUR DAFT BIRD BREAK MY WINDOW?

The house-owner was keen to give Zapp something . . . and it WASN'T money!

YOU VANDAL! I'LL FLATTEN YOU!

Jack and Curly stayed around to watch the fun.

ZAW-HAW! LOOK AT THEM RUN!

On their way home, Curly saw something that he thought Jack would like to see.

SANTA'S GROTTO NOW OPEN

LET'S GO IN HERE, JACK!

And when the boys stepped inside . . .

SANTA'S WORKSHOP

ZOWEE! WHAT A WONDERFUL PLACE!

After Jack had marvelled at the Christmas grotto, the lads headed back through the store.

ZULP! IT'S ZAPP AND HE'S RIDING A FLYING ZUMBO!

ZAW-HAW! I'LL TAKE THAT MONEY-BOX!

The shop's security guards arrived quickly on the scene, but as they approached the Zumbo, it raised its mighty trunk, and fired a strange ray.

FIX THEM, MY TRUSTY BEAST!

STOP! WHAT'S THE GAME?

Outside, Jack and Curly watched the Flying Zumbo carry off the villain.

THE BRUTE IS OUT OF CONTROL! ZAPP HAS NO IDEA WHERE HE'LL END UP!

READ THE DANDY

37

IVAN DRIVER AUTO SPARES

And with Zapp out of the way, Jack had a great idea!

CAPTAIN ZAPP'S SHIP MUST BE NEARBY. WITH THIS GADGET, I CAN TRACK IT DOWN BEFORE HE GETS BACK!

Jack's little box worked a treat, and very soon . . .

THERE'S HIS SHIP! THIS IS OUR CHANCE TO FIX CAPTAIN ZAPP!

Inside the ship, Curly was about to smash the duplicator machine that had caused all the trouble.

WAIT! I'VE AN EVEN BETTER IDEA!

DUPLICATOR

Jack still had his ticket from Santa's grotto.

I'M GOING TO USE THIS TO GET RID OF ZAPP!

GROTTO TICKET ADMIT 1

EH? BUT HOW?

Jack carried out his plan, then the boys stepped outside, just in time to see Captain Zapp return, his Flying Zumbo once more under control.

THE GAME'S UP, ZAPP! WE'VE PUT AN END TO YOUR EVIL SCHEMES!

ZAH! A COUPLE OF KIDS CAN'T STOP ME!

Jack had been busy using the villain's duplicator machine, and from the picture on his grotto ticket he'd created a whole army of Santas on flying sleighs.

ZOWEE!

PERHAPS NOT! BUT THEY CAN!

Visits to food take-away shops—Help Tom Tum come out on tops!

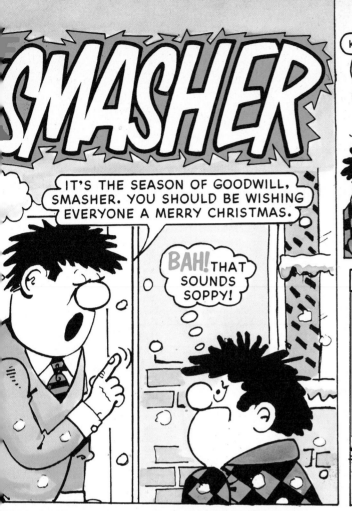

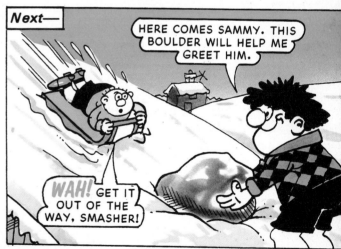

DESPERATE DAWG

THE WHOLE TOWN WILL BE WATCHING THIS FIGHT, DEPUTY. DESPERATE DAWG AND THE MAULER ARE TWO MIGHTY TOUGH GUYS.

DOGGIE PATCH GYMNASIUM

GRAND BOXING MATCH
DESPERATE DAWG
V
THE MUTTVILLE MAULER
TOMORROW

OOF!

CRASH!

DOGGIE PATCH GYMNASIUM

THAT'S DESPERATE DAWG'S SPARRING PARTNER!

I'VE HAD ENOUGH!

DOGGIE PATCH GYMNASIUM

THERE GOES ANOTHER OF DESPERATE DAWG'S SPARRING PARTNERS!

CRASH!

DOGGIE PATCH GYMNASIUM

WE'RE RUNNING OUT OF SPARRING PARTNERS FOR YOU.

I ONLY TAPPED HIM LIGHTLY!

THERE GOES THE LAST SPARRING PARTNER. THERE'S NOBODY ELSE WILLING TO SPAR WITH HIM!

CRASH!

SPLOOSH!

HORSE TROUGH

I'VE GOT TO HAVE ANOTHER SPARRING PARTNER, SHERIFF! I'LL NEED PLENTY OF PRACTICE TO FIGHT THE MAULER.

LET ME SEE! I THINK I HAVE AN IDEA.

THE TRICKS OF SCREWY DRIVER

FETCH A SHOVEL AND CLEAR THE SNOW FROM THE PATH, SCREWY.

RIGHTO, DAD!

Soon—

PHEW! THIS IS HARD WORK!

So, in the shed—

I'LL MAKE A SNOW-CLEARING MACHINE.

THUMP! BANG!

HURRAH! IT'S WORKING A TREAT!

CRUMBS! I MUST HAVE HIT A STONE BURIED IN THE SNOW.

OH, NO! ALL THE PETROL HAS SPILLED OUT AND THERE'S NONE LEFT IN THE CAN!

A few streets away—

AHA!

I'M FINISHED WITH THESE HOT CINDERS.

HEE-HEE! I'LL BORROW THIS BIN FOR A FEW MINUTES.

A FEW OF THESE HOT CINDERS ON OUR PATH WILL SOON MELT THE SNOW.

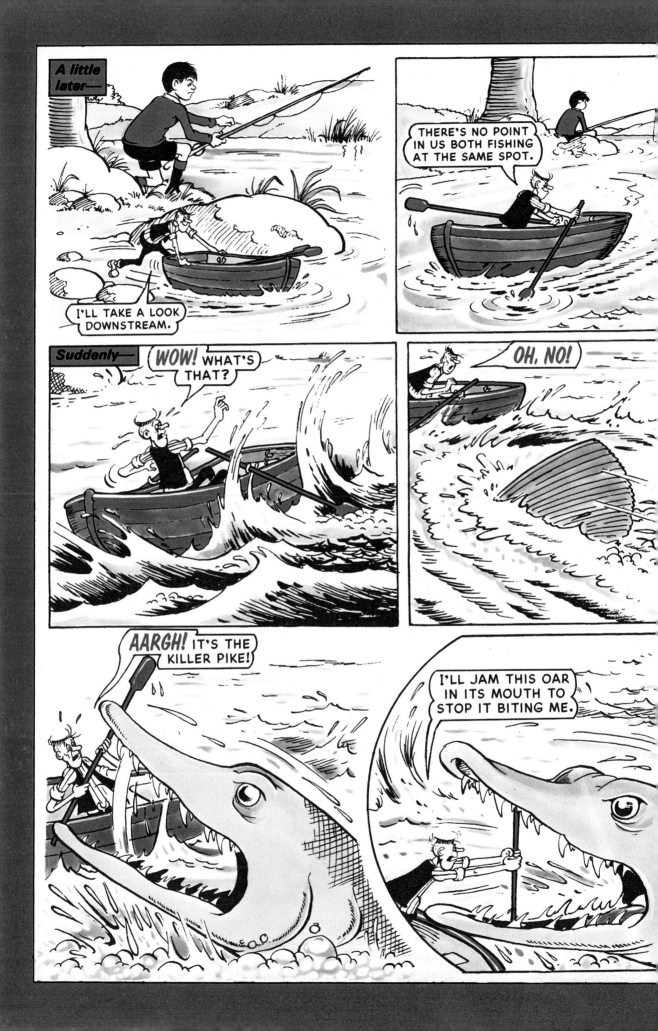

So—

...AND SO THE HOTEL OWNER HAS CONTROL OF THE PIKE WHICH IS EATING THE FISH IN THE RIVER. HE'S HOPING TO FORCE YOU TO SELL OUT AT HIS PRICE!

WE'LL FIX HIM!

GRANDPA'S GOT A PLAN!

BE CAREFUL, GRANDPA.

NOW TO LOWER MY FISHING NET INTO THE WATER.

I'LL POSITION THE NET OVER THE PIPE ENTRANCE.

AHA! THE PIKE'S IN THE NET!

WOWEE! WHAT A BIG BRUTE!

Soon—

PARK

AAAA...

OH, NO! NOT AGAIN!

CHUCKLE!

JEEPERS!

TISHOOO!

ER—SORRY, FOLKS!

HMM! I WONDER.

I SAY THERE, HARRY. COU[LD] YOU BRING HIPPO OVER TO MY HOUSE THIS AFTERNOON?

OKAY, MISTER BINKS!

So, later—

COME ON IN!

AAAAA...

GULP!

TISHOOO

100 TODAY

THANKS! JUST WHAT I WANTED! I WOULDN'T HAVE HAD THE PUFF TO BLOW OUT A HUNDRED CANDLES!

EH?

100 TODAY

SO THAT'S WHY YOU ASKED US HERE.

JOIN THE PARTY! EAT UP!

BAH!

GOBBLE!

NOSH!

YUM!

POP